TREASURES FROM POLAND

The Art Institute of Chicago
Philadelphia Museum of Art
The National Gallery of Canada
1966–1967

TREASURES FROM POLAND

A Loan Exhibition from The State Art Collection of Wawel Castle; Cracow; The Treasury of Wawel Cathedral; The National Museum of Cracow; and The National Museum of Warsaw.

Organized by The Art Institute of Chicago

Frontispiece:
65   Bellotto: View of Warsaw from Praga

That assembling an exhibition of this importance involves the participation of many persons is a fact that need hardly be expressed. Our regret is that we cannot possibly mention in this brief space all of those whose labors and talents have so cheerfully been put at our disposal. We must first of all, however, thank the Polish museum personnel and officials, who have unselfishly deprived themselves of some of their most cherished national treasures so that we in this hemisphere could enjoy them for a brief while. The exhibition contains objects from The State Art Collection at Wawel Castle, Cracow; The National Museum of Cracow; The Treasury of Wawel Castle; and The National Museum of Warsaw. We are much indebted to these institutions and their staffs for their wholehearted cooperation. The organizing committee of the exhibition—Dr. Jerzy Banach, Director of the National Museum of Cracow; Prof. Dr. Stanislaw Lorentz, Director of the National Museum of Warsaw; and Prof. Dr. Jerzy Szablowski, Director of the State Art Collection at Wawel Castle have, with taste and great knowledge of their country's cultural heritage, assembled from the treasures in their keeping an exhibition which unerringly highlights some of the most brilliant episodes of Polish history. To Dr. Lorentz and his staff go our especial thanks for compiling the catalogue of the exhibition. To the executive committee—Mgr. Jozef Kojdecki, Vice Director of the National Museum of Warsaw; Prof. Dr. Bohdan Marconi, General Curator of the National Museum of Warsaw; and Dr. Zdzislaw Zygulski, Curator of the National Museum of Cracow, go our heartfelt thanks for their astute handling of the innumerable details involved in an exhibition of this scope. The details of organizing the tour for this hemisphere were arranged by John Maxon, Associate Director of The Art Institute of Chicago, who had the invaluable help of Dr. Alexander Rytel, of Chicago, and Henryk Walenda, cultural attaché of the Polish Embassy in Washington.

Jean Sutherland Boggs, *Director of The National Gallery of Canada*
Charles C. Cunningham, *Director of The Art Institute of Chicago*
Evan H. Turner, *Director of The Philadelphia Museum of Art*

INTRODUCTION

This exhibition has been organized to commemorate the Millennium of Poland, celebrated in the years 1960-1966. It is, of course, impossible to represent the complete development of a country's art throughout 1,000 years; but we have chosen outstanding masterpieces which illuminate Polish culture and art in successive periods of the nation's history, beginning with the 11th century and ending with the first half of the 19th. Included are works by Polish artists, as well as those done by foreign artists who devoted themselves to Polish subjects, thus showing Poland's active relations with the main centers of European art. The exhibition does not attempt to cover the last part of the 19th century nor contemporary art: this period, with its new forms of expression, would require a separate exhibition.

The beginnings of the Polish state date back to the 7th and 8th centuries of our era. In the 9th century, the main centers were Gniezno and Cracow. In the middle of the 9th century, the capital of Poland was established in Gniezno, the home of Mieszko I, who in 966 was converted to Christianity, thus bringing Poland into the ranks of independent states of Central and Western Europe. In the 11th century, the capital of Poland was transferred to Cracow. The three main districts of Poland at that time were Great Poland (Wielkopolska), with its main towns, Gnizno and Poznan; Silesia (Slask), with Wroclaw; and Little Poland (Malopolska), with Cracow.

The Romanesque period in Poland, from the 11th through the first half of the 13th century, is represented by many large brick buildings and small stone churches, both ornamented with sculptures and reliefs. The centuries, however, and the devastations of wars have spared few objects from this period. Romanesque art, therefore, is marked in this exhibition by a few pieces only, including a gold chalice and paten from Tyniec, near Cracow. The Gothic period, on the other hand, is represented by more numerous outstanding pieces, some connected with princes of the Piast dynasty, who ruled in Poland between the 10th and the 14th centuries. The chalice and paten of 1240, for instance, was commissioned by Prince Konrad, who reigned in the Mazowsze district, where Warsaw is now. The bust of St. Sigismund, a gift of Casimir the Great to the Cathedral in Plock, is decorated with a princely diadem of the Piast family; and the great cross from Wawel Cathedral is made of two Piast diadems.

Gothic sculpture and painting are represented in examples of the 15th century, among them the original and charming Madonna and Child from a little church in Kruzlowa, near Cracow. The art of Wit Stwosz, who created the magnificent great altar in St. Mary's Church in Cracow, is represented in the exhibition by a figure of a knight, of about 1480, and a crucifix that might perhaps be a model for the great stone sculpture in St. Mary's. The chasuble of Kmita from Wawel Cathedral marks the turn of the Gothic and Renaissance periods.

The second group of exhibits represents the period of the Renaissance in Poland, covering the reign of the last two kings of Jagellonian dynasty, Sigismund and Sigismund Augustus. This period, from the beginning of the 16th century until 1572, marks the "Golden Age" of Poland, then a powerful state with a lively intellectual and artistic life. The Royal Palace in Cracow, built and expanded in Romanesque and Gothic times, was then given a Renaissance architecture, with emphasis on the great arcaded courtyard. In the 16th century, more than 300 tapestries adorned the walls of the Royal Palace, among them the great series ordered in Brussels by Sigismund Augustus. Eight of these tapestries are included in the exhibition. Decorative sculptures in the Royal Palace are represented by six polychrome heads from the ceiling coffers of the Hall of Deputies. Fourteen tiles show the decorative art of the Palace. Two swords are the symbols of royal power: the first, bearing the inscription "Sigismundus Rex Iustus" probably served Sigismund during the accolade ceremonies. The sword, an outstanding masterpiece of the goldsmith's art, is also a fascinating historical document. At the funeral of Sigismund Augustus, the last of his line, the sword was broken twice. In addition to the Royal Palace, an important center of culture in Cracow was the University, which solemnly celebrated its 600th anniversary in 1964. Its most illustrious student was the great astronomer Nicolaus Copernicus. We have included in the exhibition maces of University rectors of this period, as well as a portrait of Copernicus, painted in the middle of the 16th century.

The third group represents the age of the Baroque, and marks a certain Polish trend, the so-called "Sarmatian Poland" referring to the alleged origin of the Poles from the ancient Sarmatians. The main figure of this period is Jan III Sobieski, who vanquished the Turks at Vienna in 1683. Polish art of this period brings the development of portrait painting, very popular in Poland since the Renaissance, through the Age of Enlightenment in the 18th century, and, later, in the 19th century.

The fourth group is formed of masterpieces of the Age of Enlightenment in Poland, during the reign of Stanislas Augustus Poniatowski. The coronation sword of 1764, the sceptre and chain of the Order of the White Eagle, are all connected with this king. Polish costume is represented by the "Kontusz", an overcoat with split sleeves, and sashes that were worn with this costume. The Age of Enlightenment marks a lively development in art and culture in Poland. Intellectual life centered in Warsaw, at that time a great capital with over 100,000 inhabitants. Warsaw of this period is depicted in twenty-seven paintings by Bernardo Bellotto, who arrived in Warsaw in 1767 and remained there until his death in 1780. Eleven of these views of Warsaw are included in the exhibition; the twelfth Bellotto is a painting representing the election of Stanislas Augustus Poniatowski. The art of portrait painting continued to be very popular, and many Poles traveling abroad had their portraits painted by foreign artists. An example in the exhibition is the magnificent portrait of Count Stanislas Kostka-Potocki by David, a masterpiece of French painting.

The fifth group in the exhibition embraces painting of the 19th century. The most eminent Polish painter of the Romantic Era was Piotr Michalowski, represented here with six canvases. A different facet of Romanticism is shown by the Wankowicz portrait of Poland's great poet, Adam Mickiewicz. Another important portrait painter was Henryk Rodakowski, whose most outstanding painting, the portrait of his mother, is included in the exhibition. Two canvases by Jan Matejko close the exhibition. This painter's romantic views of historical scenes create an imaginative vision of Polish history through the centuries.

Owing to the span of time covered by the exhibition, and the diversity of objects of art presented, I have discussed them in this introduction in groups, and in chronological order. Each piece in the exhibition possesses, however, its own artistic expression: not only does each contribute its share of history, but also speaks for itself.

Stanislaw Lorentz, *Director, The National Museum of Warsaw*

CATALOGUE

1 Chalice and Paten

Rhineland, second half of the 11th century. a) The Chalice. Gold, stamped and repoussé. Height 9.2 cm., diameter 7.2 cm., weight 198.55 grams. Inv. no. Dep. 362. b) The Paten, with the Hand of Providence represented on a cross emerging from the sky. Gold, stamped and repoussé. Diameter 8.8 cm., weight 37.87 grams. Inv. no. Dep. 362.

The chalice represents the so-called *calix viaticus*. It was found in 1961, in an abbot's grave in Tyniec, near Cracow, during archeological research on the site of a Benedictine Abbey. It is an extremely rare example of early romanesque goldsmiths' art, closely tied with Polish medieval culture, and the most ancient monument of this kind in Polish Collections. *(illustrated)*

The State Art Collection of Wawel Castle, Cracow

2 Virgin and Child Enthroned

Late 12th century. Lime wood, gesso, polychrome. Height 40 cm. Inv. no. 1 (formerly 75342)

The earliest specimen of romanesque wooden sculpture preserved in Poland. The statue served as a reliquary, as indicated by a hollow in the throne where the relics were kept. In spite of the fact that the statue was damaged considerably, the original polychrome has been partly preserved. The sculpture comes from a Cistercian convent established in 1213 in Olobok in Great Poland (Wielkopolska).

The National Museum of Warsaw

3 Stole

Poland or South Germany, early 13th century. Embroidery, silk, gold thread. a) Height 70 cm., width 4.5 cm. b) Height 66 cm., width 4 cm.

These two fragments of a stole are decorated with designs representing the "Sacerdotium," and a semi-anthemion tendril. Their style points to various sources, with South German and Italian ones predominating. This stole is the earliest specimen among embroideries preserved in Poland. It comes from a collegiate church in Kruszwica, one of the main centers of Poland during the formation of the Polish state. It was found in a grave during excavations in 1961.

Collegiate Church, Kruszwica

4 Chalice and Paten

Gift of Prince Konrad Mazowiecki. Plock, 1238. a) The Chalice. Silver gilt with parts stamped on model forms; engraved decorative elements; the nodus is cast. Height 21 cm., diameter 18 cm., weight 890 grams. Inv. no. SZ.995/1–2MN. *(illustrated)*

The outside face of the bowl is decorated with engravings. An inscription in Roman majuscules reads *"dvx conradus boleslaws, emomizl, mesc, lvdmila, salomea, indita, ivdita."* The bowl is encircled by eight medallions presenting the following scenes: 1) Angel, 2) Virgin Mary (Annunciation), 3) The Manger, 4) St. Joseph (The Nativity), 5) Virgin Mary and the King, 6) Two Kings (Adoration of the Magi), 7) Massacre of the Innocents, 8) The Flight into Egypt. On a coniform bush stand Christ Crucified and the figures of St. John the Baptist and the prophets Jeremiah, Isaiah, Abraham, Moses, and Elias, with their names on ribbons. b) The Paten. Silver gilt, repoussé, engraved. Height 11.5 cm., diameter 21 cm., weight 280 grams. Inv. no. SZM.995/1–2.MN. In the middle of an hexafoil bottom are engraved figure scenes: Christ the Pantocrator enthroned is in the center; over His head an angel holds a censer. On both sides, four kneeling figures form an antithetic composition. In the upper part on the left, a woman's figure holds a chalice, and the inscription *"oafia"*; on the right, a male figure also holds a chalice, and an inscription *"dvx conradus"*; below, two male figures and two inscriptions, on the left, *"hazimirus,"* on the right, *"semovitvs."* The chalice and paten were offered by Prince Konrad Mazowiecki to the Cathedral in Plock, in expiation for the assassination of the Canon Jan Czapla. This monument of Polish art is all the more precious because of its close links with the historical importance of the donors (who are represented on the paten), and for the fact that it was made on special order.

The National Museum of Warsaw

5 Bust of Saint Sigismund

Reliquary, gift of King Casimir the Great to the Cathedral in Plock. The crown contains fragments of Piast crowns. 1370. a) The Bust. Silver, repoussé, partly gilt; silver soldering fitted with silver thread; engraved; sapphire in a cabochon setting. Height 35 cm., width 36.5 cm., depth 23 cm., weight 4020 grams. Inv. no. SZM.996. The bust is of almost natural dimensions. The outside oblique part of the socle is encircled with the following inscription in a Gothic majuscule *"kasimirus dei.gra.rex.poloniae. sanoti. sigismvndi. procuravit. sb. a [do. mi. m. ccc.]"* (The fragment of the text in brackets is in front of the socle.) b) The Crown. Gold, plate, and lost-wax process parts engraved and chiseled; flat parts decorated with nielli, rubies, diamonds, pearls, sapphires, and colored glass. Height 11 cm., diameter 21 cm., weight 1070 grams. Inv. no. SZM.996.MN. The crown is composed of seven large and seven smaller parts with tracery finials of trifoliated and unifoliated elements. Each part has open-work plant motifs. The larger ones have riders and kneeling and standing figures.

There are four reliquaries of this type in Polish collections. Two of them, the bust of St. Sigismund, offered to the Cathedral in Plock, and the bust of St. Mary Magdalene, offered to the church in Stopnica, are gifts of King Casimir the Great (1310–1370). The crown of this bust has some parts of Piast crowns of the thirteenth century. The reliquary was considerably damaged when the Treasury of the Cathedral was robbed, in 1520. The nose and the left arm of the bust were then damaged, and the crown was broken. Most probably the piece was repaired in Cracow, as well as the crown, which was then enriched with additional precious stones and pearls. In 1601, a goldsmith of Plock, Jan Zemelka, repaired the crown once more and strengthened it inside with a silver plate, adding also a late-Renaissance band and a silver cupola to cover the relics.

The National Museum of Warsaw

6 The Virgin and Child from Kruzlowa

Lime wood, gesso, polychrome. Early 15th century. Original colors have been preserved on the face and the hands. The polychrome on the vestments has been partly reconstructed. Height 118 cm. Inv. no. MNK.I.10.315. *(illustrated)*

One of the most remarkable Gothic sculptures in Poland, and one of the leading masterpieces of European art in the period of about 1400. The statue represents the "beautiful" or the "international" style in vogue at that time. This sculpture from a little parish church in Kruzlowa, in Little Poland (Malopolska), although belonging to a large group of "Beautiful Madonnas" of Czech, Austrian, and Silesian origin, yet has some distinct features—a greater simplicity and a very subtle lyrical expression—showing that it pertained to the Cracow School.

The National Museum of Cracow

7 Crucifixion of Korzenna

Tempera on wood, gesso, gilt ground. 117 × 65 cm. Second quarter of the 15th century. Inv. no. MNK.I.7.787.

The painting comes from a parish church in Korzenna, near Nowy Sacz, (Little Poland), and is probably a fragment of a lost triptych. Because of its formal values, indicating a conversance with the art of the *trecento* in Italy, and its profound and severe style, it ranks among the leading paintings of Little Poland from the fifteenth century.

The National Museum of Cracow

8 Cardinal's Mace

Gift of the Cardinal Zbigniew Olesnicki to the Jagellonian University. Silver gilt; relief casting chiseled and engraved. Cracow, before 1455. Length 115.9 cm., weight 2360 grams. Inv. no. 34/SK.

Within the crown's circumference three coats of arms are incised: 1) St. Peter's Keys under a papal tiara, 2) The Polish-Lithuanian emblem under a crown, 3) The "Debno," arms of the Olesnicki family, under a cardinal's hat. An inscription engraved on the shank in a Gothic minuscule reads "Scep/trum/p/atris/ d/omini/ sbignei t/i/t/uli s/an/c/t/e prisce p/res/it/er/i craco/viensi/ legatum obiit fer/iat/er/cia p/pst/

palmar/ vm/a/nno d/omini/ m° ccc° lv." At the bottom of the crown, four coats of arms are soldered: 1) "Debno," 2) Polish Eagle, 3) Five Eagles of Lower Austria, 4) an empty one added during a renovation to replace a former bearing which disappeared, and which undoubtedly contained the arms of the Habsburgs. In the fifteenth century the mace was usually carried before a cardinal during official ceremonies. The mace of Zbigniew Olesnicki (d.1455) was offered to him by King Casimir the Jagellon (1427–1492) and his wife Queen Elizabeth, daughter of the Habsburg Emperor Albrecht II. After the death of the cardinal, as the inscription on the shank reads, the mace became the property of the Jagellonian University.

The Museum of the Jagellonian University, Cracow

9 The Miter of Bishop Tomasz Strzempinski

Silk, red satin, pearls, gold, silver gilt, semi-precious stones, 1455–1460, and about 1530. 40.5 cm. × 31 cm. Length of lappets 44 cm.

The miter was made for Bishop Strzempinski (his coat of arms, the "Prus," appears on the lappets). It is possible that the miter was made in Italy, as the bishop remained in close contact with this country, when professor at the Jagellonian University, and, later, in 1432–1443, its rector; and also while attending the Council of Basel. From this period come the silver gilded *circulus* and *titulus*. Embroideries on the triangles and lappets were added while the miter was being renovated in 1530, thanks to the endeavors of Bishop Piotr Tomicki. The design was most probably made by the Cracow painter Stanislaw Samostrzelnik.

The Treasury of Wawel Cathedral, Cracow

10 The Marys from Niegowicia

Tempera on wood, about 1470. 90 × 72 cm. Inv. no. MNK.I.135.177.

The painting is a fragment of a composition, *The Three Marys at the Tomb*, which has not been preserved in its entirety. It comes from a parish church in Niegowicia, near Bochnia in Little Poland, and probably formed part of a lost altar. The faces of the women, the scale of colors, with intensive dark red and olive-green dominating, as well as

the formal values of the painting, allow us to attribute this work to the *atelier* of an anonymous Cracovian master, the Master of the Choirs.

The National Museum of Cracow

11 Scenes from the Life of the Virgin

Tempera on wood, about 1470. 40.5 × 25.5 cm. The frames measure 58 × 43.5 cm. Inv. no. Dep. 9–8.

These two small paintings come from a chapel of the furriers' guild in the Church of the Virgin Mary, Cracow, and they were painted in a Cracow studio. The original frames have been preserved; they are ornamented and silver-gilt, with tiny reliquaries set in glazed rhombs.

The National Museum of Cracow

12 Two Wings of the Mikuszowice Altar

Tempera on wood, gesso, gilt ground, about 1470. The upper quarters are 102 × 70 cm., the lower quarters, which were cut down at an unknown period, are 55 × 70 cm. Inv. no. Dep. 20–21. *(illustrated)*

On the obverse, left, are St. Gregory the Great and St. Jerome; at right are St. Augustine and St. Ambrose. On the reverse, left, are The Vocation of SS. Peter and Andrew and The Vision of St. John the Evangelist on the Isle of Patmos; at right are the Flight of St. Paul from Damascus and St. Philip Converting the Treasurer of Queen Kandaka. The triptych to which the wings belong comes from a church in Mikuszowice, near Biala, in Little Poland. Originally, however, it was placed in Cracow Cathedral. It was created in the studio of the Master of Choirs.

The National Museum of Cracow

13 Cross Made of Princely Crowns

Cracow, 1472–1488. Cypress wood, covered with gold plate; diamonds, rubies, emeralds, pearls, and other precious stones. Height 83.8 cm., width 58 cm., weight 5080 grams. *(illustrated)*

The first crown has been laid on the transverse arm of the cross, and it contains twelve parts, with niello cases adorned with eagles, figures of fighting knights, and hunting scenes. The second crown, laid on the longer, vertical arm is considerably damaged. It contains fourteen parts adorned with eagles. The two crowns are traditionally linked with Prince Boleslaw Wstydliwy (the Shy), who died in 1279, and with his wife the Beatified Kinga (d.1292). The crowns were probably made in Venice in the first half of the thirteenth century. In the second half of the fifteenth century, when the cross was being made of these diadems, with precious stones and pearls added, the lower part of the cross was emblazoned with the Polish Eagle, the Three Crowns (the sign of the Cracow Chapter), and "Polkozic," the arms of the Cracow Bishop, Jan Rzeszowski.

The Treasury of Wawel Cathedral, Cracow

14 The Knight

Lime wood, polychrome, gesso, after 1480. Length 108 cm. Inv. no. MNK I–2.088.

The provenance of the statue is the Church of the Virgin Mary in Cracow, where it probably served as a guard for the setting of the Holy Sepulcher during Holy Week, or as a shield holder supporting a coat of arms. The original idea of the knightly figure, presented in complex motion, with the sharp features of the face, and the precise workmanship of the Gothic armor, allow us to presume that the sculpture is the work of Wit Stwosz himself, who was working at that time on the Mariacki Altar.

The National Museum of Cracow

15 Crucifix

Lime wood, some remnants of the original polychrome, gesso, after 1491. Height 47.5 cm. The left hand, fingers of the right hand, and fragments of the toes are reconstructed. Inv. no. MNK L–5.004.

A valuable work of the Cracow school of sculpture of the late medieval period. Its style, arrangement of the body, and, most particularly, the decorative treatment of the perizonium show close links with the art of Wit Stwosz. *(illustrated)*

The National Museum of Cracow

16 Rector's Mace

Gift of the Cardinal Frideric the Jagellon to the Jagellonian University. Silver gilt; embossed relief; engraved; red and black enamel. Cracow, 1493. Length 108 cm., weight 1090 grams. Inv. no. 35/SK.

The royal goldsmith, Marcin Marciniec (d.1518), was from a well-known goldsmiths' family in Cracow of the beginning of the fifteenth century. He was a citizen and councillor of Cracow, and worked in that town between 1486 and 1518. On the top of the head of the mace are coats of arms: 1) Pope Alexander VI, with a papal tiara and St. Peter's Keys, 2) The Polish Eagle, with a metropolitan cross and a cardinal's hat, 3) Habsburgs' arms, with a crown over a shield. The Habsburgs' arms would indicate that the mace was ordered by the mother of the Cardinal Frideric the Jagellon (d.1503), Queen Elizabeth (see no. 8), most probably to celebrate the occasion of her son's receiving the purple in 1493.

The Museum of the Jagellonian University, Cracow

17 Descent from the Cross

Tempera on wood, gesso, 1495. 214 × 146 cm. Inv. no. 44 (formerly 184984). *(illustrated)*

One of the three paintings of the Passion from St. John's Church in Torun. The remaining two represent the Flagellation (at present in the National Museum of Warsaw) and the Crowning with Thorns (lost during the last war). On the original frame of the picture, which no longer exists, a date was inserted. An interesting detail here are portraits of the donor's family painted on an already finished composition. A similar addition of the donor's portrait can also be seen on the Flagellation. The painter of this Descent from the Cross, probably a master from Pomerania, was working under the influence of Netherlandish painting.

The National Museum of Warsaw

18 Altar with the Legend of Saint Stanislas

Tempera on wood, gesso, about 1500. 90 × 65 cm. Inv. no. Dep. 162, 163.

Two quarters of the altarpiece are shown. On the obverse are The Punishment of Unfaithful Wives and The Execution of the King's Verdict on Stanislaw Szczepanowski, Bishop of Cracow; on the reverse are The Entombment of St. Stanislas and The Canonization of St. Stanislas (see no. 19, *Chasuble of Kmita,* for more information on St. Stanislas). The paintings come from St. Stanislas' Church in Szczepanwo. It is a work of an unknown Cracovian master from the circles close to the Master of the Altar with the Legend of St. John the Almoner.

The State Art Collection of Wawel Castle, Cracow

19 *Chasuble with the Life of Saint Stanislas*

Cloth-of-gold (velours-de-Gênes), embossed embroidery, pearls, gold. Cracow, between 1501–1505. The cross was transferred to another chasuble in the years between 1563–1586. 140 × 82 cm. *(illustrated)*

The chasuble was given by the Cracow Voivode, Piotr Kmita the Elder, Master of Wisnicz, early in the 16th century. On the cross of the chasuble are embroidered scenes from the life of St. Stanislas, Poland's patron saint, and bishop of Cracow, who was condemned to death by King Boleslaw Smialy (the Bold) in 1079. The scenes are: 1) Purchase of a Village, 2) Resuscitation of Piotrowin, 3) Testimony in the Presence of the King, 4) The Death of St. Stanislas, 5) Dismembering of the Corpse, 6) Funeral, 7) Canonization. There is also a half-figure of a man holding the "Szreniawa" coat of arms, with a ribbon carrying an embossed inscription in minuscule *"petrus de/wysznitze palentinus [sic]/palatinus cracoviensis [1] 50 [. .]."* In 1563–1586, the cross was transferred to another older chasuble made of cloth-of-gold (velours-de-Gênes), most probably in Venice early in the second half of the fifteenth century. Hence, on the front of the chasuble appears a late-Renaissance emblem of the Cracow Chapter, the Three Crowns.

The Treasury of Wawel Cathedral, Cracow

20–31 *TILES*

A set of colorful ceramic stove tiles in glazed relief, from the Royal Castle of Wawel, Cracow, represent Polish ceramic art of the late fifteenth century and the first half of the sixteenth century. The tiles, shattered into fragments, were found on the territory of the Wawel. Some of them were discovered in 1927 under the pavement of the Castle's gallery, during repair work, others were found in 1939 on the Wawel Hill. Some of the tiles were made at Bartosz's of Kazimierz in Cracow, who was working there at the turn of the fifteenth and the sixteenth century. While looking over the tiles exhibited here, an evolution in the style of Polish ceramic art can be noticed, beginning with a Gothic decorative motif (the tile with the image of King Olbracht), up to the Renaissance (armorial tiles, and the one with a cherub, inspired by antique models). The technique of Wawel tiles includes various glazes—lead glaze, tin-lead glaze, as well as a large variety of colors.

20 *Tile with a Stag*

Cracow, 15th/16th century. Argil, relief, lead glaze in dark green and olive-yellow. Height 21.5 cm., width 22.5 cm. Inv. no. 4295.

21 *Tile with a Griffin*

Cracow, 15th/16th century. Argil, relief, lead glaze in yellow. Height 22 cm., width 22.5 cm. Inv. no. 4270

22 *Tile with Polish Eagle*

Cracow, first quarter of the 16th century. Argil, relief, lead glaze in green and cream yellow. Height 21 cm., width 21 cm. Inv. no. 4310.

23 *Tile with King Jan Olbracht*

Cracow, first quarter of the 16th century. Made at Bartosz's of Kazimierz, Argil, relief, tin-lead glaze in green, white, yellow, cobalt-blue, and brown-violet. Height 40.5 cm., width 23.5 cm. Inv. no. 4303. *(illustrated)*

24 *Tile with Rosette*

Cracow, first quarter of the 16th century. Made at Bartosz's of Kazimierz. Argil, relief, tin-lead glaze in green, white, yellow, blue, and brown-violet. Height 22.5 cm., width 22.5 cm. Inv. no. 4288.

25 Tile with Pomegranate

Cracow, first quarter of the 16th century. Made at Bartosz's of Kazimierz. Argil, relief, tin-lead glaze in green, white, yellow, blue, brown-violet. Height 22.5 cm., width 22.5 cm. Inv. no. 4316.

26 Tile with Rosette

Cracow, first quarter of the 16th century. Made at Bartosz's of Kazimierz. Argil, relief, tin-lead glaze in green, white, orange, and dark blue. Height 21.5 cm., width 21 cm. Inv. no. 4271.

27 Tile with Rosette

Cracow, first quarter of the 16th century. Made at Bartosz's of Kazimierz. Argil, relief, tin-lead glaze in green, white, yellow, blue, and brown-violet. Height 22.5 cm., width 22 cm. Inv. no. 4282.

28 Tile

With the Polish Eagle of King Sigismund I, the Old, and the letter "S." Cracow, second quarter of the 16th century. Argil, relief, tin-lead glaze in white, yellow, cobalt-blue, brown-violet. Height 18.5 cm., width 18.5 cm. Inv. no. 4430.

29 Tile

With the Sforza family coat of arms (serpent devouring a child) of Queen Bona, Wife of Sigismund I, the Old. Cracow, second quarter of the 16th century. Argil, relief, tin-lead glaze in white, yellow, green, cobalt-blue, and brown-violet. Height 19 cm., width 19 cm. Inv. no. 4429.

30 Tile with a Cherub

Cracow, second quarter of the 16th century. Argil, relief, tin-lead glaze in white, turquoise, green, cobalt-blue, and brown-violet. Height 24.5 cm., width 19 cm. Inv. no. 4422.

31 Tile Frieze with Dolphins and Flowers

Cracow, second quarter of the 16th century. Argil, relief, tin-lead glaze in white, yellow, turquoise-green, cobalt-blue, and brown-violet. Height 16.5 cm., width 20.5 cm. Inv. no. 4419.

The State Art Collection of Wawel Castle, Cracow

32 Sword of King Sigismund I, the Old

Steel, silver gilt, and engraved. Cracow, first quarter of the 16th century. Length 120 cm., width 19.8 cm., weight 1915 grams. Inv. no. 3989.

On the steel blade is a wolf, the sign of the town of Passau. The hilt, with a cross guard and shield, and scabbard are silver gilt with engraved coats of arms of Poland and Lithuania, the figure of the king, and an inscription on a band: *sigismundus rex justus*. The sword was made for King Sigismund I, the Old (1467–1548). The inventory of the Crown Treasury marks the sword as the one used for the accolade celebrations. In 1795, it was stolen from Wawel by the Prussians, together with other royal coronation insignia. In 1951, the sword was purchased in London and offered to the Wawel Collection by a group of Poles.

The State Art Collection of Wawel Castle, Cracow

33 Horn of the Wieliczka Salt Miners

Bison's horn set in silver, precision casting work engraved and chiseled, 1534. Height 36 cm., width 47 cm., depth 15 cm. *(illustrated)*

The oval stand in the form of a rock holds the figure of Hercules bearing the horn. On the smooth surface of the upper fitting are coats of arms: 1) Eagle of King Sigismund I, the Old, with a letter "S" on the chest, 2) Serpent of Queen Bona Sforza, wife of King Sigismund, the Old, 3) Bonar, 4) Ogonczyk, 5) Emblems of Wieliczka salt miners—hammer, pickax, and trumpets. The date is 1534. The horn was a gift offered to the salt miners of Wieliczka by Seweryn Bonar, a Cracow burgher and owner of a salt mine in Wieliczka, and his wife Jadwiga Koscielecka.

The National Museum of Cracow

34 Sword of Sigismund I, the Old, and of Sigismund Augustus

Steel; silver gilt, relief, cast, engraved; silver cord. Made at Melchior Baier's, designed by Peter Flötner, Nuremberg 1540. Length 104 cm., width 23 cm. *(illustrated)*

On the pommel, on the guard, and on the chape are plant ornaments; the small of the sheath has on the obverse the scene of Hercules fighting with Antaeus, and the date 1540. The sheath and the grip of the hilt are made of silver thread plaited to imitate jersey stitch. The sword was twice broken in 1572 at the funeral of the last king of the Jagellonian Dynasty, Sigismund Augustus (1520–1572), according to the custom binding at the funerals of the last male descendants of a family.

The Treasury of Wawel Cathedral, Cracow

35 Silver Bird

Emblem of the Cracow Shooting Fraternity, about 1565. Silver, hammered and chiseled. Height 42 cm. Original case, dimensions 45 × 38 × 18 cm. Weight, together with chain, 3.05 kg. Inv. no. 198/Br.K.

The bird, forged in silver with detailed feathering, raised wings, and an arched crown on its head, is on a stand shaped like a branch. In spite of its name, it resembles an eagle rather than a cock. That it is said to be the gift of Sigismund Augustus in 1565 to the Cracow Shooting Fraternity can be confirmed by the style of the piece.
The Shooting Fraternity of Cracow has traditions dating back to the Middle Ages. The aim of the Fraternity was to train the townsfolk in the use of arms, so that they could defend the city walls in case of war. Bows and crossbows were used at first, and then, exclusively, firearms. The target was a cock made of wood, posed on a high perch. The best marksman won the title of "king," and was privileged to carry the silver statue of a cock during a festive parade. This tradition is still cherished in Cracow, where every year a "king" is elected at a shooting competition of the Fraternity. *(illustrated)*

The Historical Museum of Cracow

36 Portrait of Nicolaus Copernicus

Tempera with oil glaze on an oak board, by an unknown Polish painter of the first half of the 16th century. 51.5 × 41.5 cm. On the reverse of the frame is an inscription of the late 16th century: Nicolaus Copernicus. Inv. no. Ad.217. *(illustrated)*

The great Polish scientist (1473–1543) was born in Torun, and attended the Jagellonian University in Cracow. An astronomer, mathematician, economist, and doctor, he propounded the heliocentric theory of the universe, published in 1543 in his work, *De Revolutionibus Orbium Celestium*. In style and technique, this picture shows links with the school of Pomeranian painting. A copy of this portrait, made in 1735, hangs in the Paris Astronomical Observatory.

The Pomeranian Museum of Torun

37 The Resurrection

Signed with the monogram TF (Tobiasz Fendt, d.1576 ?). Tempera on wood, 16th century. 117.5 × 83 cm. Inv. no. 337.

A fragmentary view of old Cracow appears in this picture, which comes from the Jesuit Monastery of the church of St. Barbara in Cracow.

The State Art Collection of Wawel Castle, Cracow

38–43 WAWEL HEADS

These Wawel Heads, made in Cracow by Sebastian Tauerbach (d.1553) and Jan Snycerz (d.1545), decorated the coffered ceiling of the Hall of Deputies in the Royal Castle of Wawel. Originally, there were 194 heads; today, only 30 survive. The ceiling was also decorated with 176 rosettes and three coats of arms. The heads represent figures of Cracow burghers, scientists, courtiers, legendary kings, etc. This style of ceiling decoration, where a head was placed in each coffer, though with some analogies with the decoration of the Arch of Alfonso I in Naples, is an original example that cannot be traced elsewhere in European art.

38 Man in a Prince's Hat

Lime wood, polychromed, 35 cm. high. Inv. no. 3013.

39 Man in a Renaissance Net Bonnet

Lime wood, polychromed. 35 cm. high. Inv. no. 3022. *(illustrated)*

40 Man in a Laurel Wreath

Lime wood, polychromed, 35 cm. high. Inv. no. 3027.

41 Girl with a Wreath

Lime wood, polychromed, 35 cm. high. Inv. no. 3018. *(illustrated)*

42 Warrior

Lime wood, polychromed, 35 cm. high. Inv. no. 3010.

43 Warrior in a Kapalin Helmet

Lime wood, polychromed, 35 cm. high. Inv. no. 3033.

The State Art Collection of Wawel Castle, Cracow

44–51 JAGELLONIAN TAPESTRIES

Tapestries were occasionally brought to Poland as early as the 15th century, but the nation's large collection of about 350 specimens is due to the purchases of King Sigismund I in 1526, and, particularly, to those of King Sigismund Augustus in 1548–1567. The tapestries were bought to decorate the walls of the Royal Castle at Wawel in Cracow and other royal residences in the country. Wawel Castle, which since the 10th century was constantly being enlarged, was during the first half of the 16th century thoroughly transformed in the Renaissance style, equipped with a large arcaded courtyard, and given a magnificent Renaissance interior.
The collection of tapestries was composed of three groups: 1) Biblical subjects with a series of the Garden of Eden, the Story of Noah, the Story of Moses, and the Tower of Babel; 2) Landscape and animal subjects; 3) Grotesque ornaments with state emblems and royal ciphers. The cartoons for figure subjects were designed by Michel Coxien. The
tapestries with animal and landscape themes were called "pugna ferrarum," for the fighting animals usually represented. They were also called "ad venationem spectantia peristromata," for their subjects related to the hunting tastes of Sigismund Augustus. These cartoons were designed by Willem Tons. The models for the grotesque series were taken from the work of Cornelis Floris and Cornelis Bos. Most of these wall tapestries were made in the best manufactories of Brussels, those of Willem Pannemaker's, Pieter van Aelst's, Jan van Tiegen's, and Nicolas Leyniers'. Today, only 136 of these tapestries have survived in Poland. During the last war they were kept in Canada, but at present they decorate once again the walls of the Castle at Wawel.

44 Tapestry

Verdure with animals, badgers in the foreground. Brussels, Pieter van Aelst, from cartoons by Willem Tons. Third quarter of the 16th century, wool, silk, gold, 436 × 126 cm. Inv. no. 164812.

The National Museum of Warsaw

45 Tapestry

Verdure with animals, duck, tortoise, and hind in the foreground. Brussels, Nicolas Leyniers, from cartoons by Willem Tons. Third quarter of the 16th century, wool, silk, gold, 433 × 140 cm. Inv. no. 164811.

The National Museum of Warsaw

46 Tapestry

Verdure with animals, hind in the foreground. Brussels, Nicolas Leyniers, from cartoons by Willem Tons. Third quarter of the 16th century, wool, silk, gold. 445 × 146 cm. Inv. no. 164809. *(illustrated)*

The National Museum of Warsaw

47 Tapestry

Verdure with animals, jaguar in the foreground. Brussels, Jan van Tiegen, from cartoons by Willem Tons. Third quarter of the 16th century, wool, silk, gold, 440 × 135 cm. Inv. no. 164810.

The National Museum of Warsaw

48 Tapestry

With the monogram of King Sigismund Augustus and satyrs. Brussels, third quarter of the 16th century, wool, silk, gold, silver, 245 × 211 cm. Inv. no. 3887. *(illustrated)*

The State Art Collection of Wawel Castle, Cracow

49 Tapestry

With the emblems of Poland and Lithuania and an allegory of Fortune. Brussels, third quarter of the 16th century, wool, silk, gold, silver, 169 × 417 cm., manufactory of Jan van Tiegen. Inv. no. 3875.

The State Art Collection of Wawel Castle, Cracow

50 Tapestry

With the emblems of Poland and Lithuania and an allegory of Glory. Brussels, third quarter of the 16th century, wool, silk, gold, silver, 148 × 283 cm., manufactory of Nicolas Leyniers. Inv. no. 3864.

The State Art Collection of Wawel Castle, Cracow

51 Tapestry

With the emblems of Poland and Lithuania and an allegory of Glory. Brussels, third quarter of the 16th century, wool, silk, gold, silver, 155 × 292 cm., manufactory of Jan van Tiegen. Inv. no. 3870.

The State Art Collection of Wawel Castle, Cracow

52 Hussar's Casque

Poland, second half of the 16th century. Steel, etched and engraved, incrusted with gold. Height 31.5 cm., width 36 cm. Inv. no. 3132.

Hussar's casques were used by Polish armored cavalry. This specimen comes from the collection of count Tyszkiewicz in Lohojsk, and was bought for the Wawel Collection in Paris, in 1934, from Benedykt Tyszkiewicz. *(illustrated)*

The State Art Collection of Wawel Castle, Cracow

53 Portrait of Sigismund Augustus

Late 16th century, oil on copper, 60 × 49 cm. Inv. no. MNK I–1446.

Sigismund Augustus (1520–1572), sovereign from 1548, was the last king of the Jagellonian dynasty. This is one of the few portraits extant of the king, and was painted by an unidentified painter working in Poland in the last part of the 16th century. The arrangement of the figure, the facial features, and the royal costume are similar to those known from a miniature made in the studio of Lucas Cranach the Younger. Most probably it is one of the copies made from the portrait used during funeral ceremonies. The rather dark scale of colors, and the accentuated *chiaroscuro* of the head, evoke some associations with contemporaneous portraits from Gdansk.

The National Museum of Cracow

54 Portrait of Anna Jagellonka

Painted after 1586, by an unidentified Warsaw painter of the second half of the 16th century. Oil on canvas, 103 × 86 cm. Inv. no. 1160-WIL. *(illustrated)*

The last representative of the Jagellonian Dynasty, Anna Jagellonka (1523–1596), was the daughter of King Sigismund I, the Old, and the Italian princess, Bona Sforza. She was sister to King Sigismund Augustus, and, from 1576, wife of the Polish King Stefan Batory. She abdicated in 1586 in favor of her nephew, Sigismund III, Waza. Anna was a protectress of the Cracow Academy (Jagellonian University in Cracow). This portrait is one of three oil images that have survived, of identical composition and similar monochromatic coloring. Its style shows some links with the painting of Marcin Kober, Stefan Batory's court painter, or with the artist's studio.

The National Museum of Warsaw, Wilanow Section

55 Death of a Rich Man

Mazowsze (Warsaw region), after 1620. Lime wood, carved in relief, polychromed and gilt. Height 53 cm., width 85 cm. Inv. no. 5021.

Against a background of illusionistic architecture of the late Renaissance, a nobleman is represented on his deathbed, surrounded by his family and assisted by a priest, a monk, and two devils. This is an example of an old medieval subject of religious, moralizing art presented in a realistic form, which expresses features of Polish Sarmatian customs of the early 17th century (see also nos. 57, 58, 86, 87, 93–108). Most probably, the relief formed the predella of the altar in the church at Sochaczew.

The National Museum of Cracow

56 Polish Costume Sabre

A "Karabela" (scimitar). Lwow. The blade dates from 1607, the scabbard from the middle of the 18th century. Steel, two-colored gold, repoussé, engraved, green enamel, nielli, diamonds, rubies, ebony, and leather. Length 96 cm., width 13.5 cm. Inv. no. SZM.913MN. *(illus.)*

The hilt is of ebony; the gold fittings are incrusted with precious stones, and, on the pommel is a feather motif in diamonds. On the obverse of the blade an inscription is incrusted in gold *"in nomine domini. vinces/ad 1607."* On the reverse is a monogram *"marya"* and the inscription *"ses.in.sanctissima.maria certa.salus.victoria."*
The scimitar served first of all as an accessory to the Polish noble costume, the overcoat with split sleeves, known as "Kontusz" and an undergarment of the national dress known as "Zupan." Sabres were usually richly ornamented, to fit the decorative style of Polish costume.

The National Museum of Warsaw

57 Hetman's Baton

Poland, second half of the 17th century. Silver gilt, engraved, embossed with rubies, turquoise, and chalcedony plates incrusted with gold. Height 72 cm., dia. 11.5 cm., weight 1475 grams. Inv. no. 507-WIL.

The baton originated in Southeast Poland, and represents the so-called "Sarmatian" trend in Polish culture (see nos. 55, 58, 86, 87, 93–108). The hetman was the supreme commander of the army in Poland from the 16th century until Poland's partition at the end of the 18th century, and the baton was a symbol of his power.

The National Museum of Warsaw, Wilanow Section

58 Coffin Portrait of Stanislaw Woysza

By an unidentified Polish painter of the late 17th century. Oil on lead, 43.4 × 47.2 cm. (sexpartite). Inscribed on the reverse: *"Jegomosc Pan Stanislaw ze Bzowa Woysza Podstoli Smolenski Pocieszenia Panny Przenaysw. Godzinek Fundator zycie doczesne/skonczyl Roku 1677 Lutego."* [Gentleman Stanislaw of Bzow/Woysza Assistant Master of the Pantry of Smolensk Founder of the Little Offices of Our Lady of Consolation ended his life on earth in February 1677.] Inv. no. 487.

An example of images placed at the head of coffins, hence the term "coffin portraits." This type of portrait is otherwise unknown in European art, and is typical of the Sarmatian trend in Polish art, between the late 16th and mid-18th centuries. Coffin portraits were usually painted by unknown artists on lead or copper plates, very often after the death of the subject. After the funeral, coffin portraits were placed on tombs, on church walls, or in sacristies. *(illustrated)*

The National Museum of Warsaw, Wilanow Section

59 Salver with Triumph of Jan III Sobieski

Gdansk, 1683, by the goldsmith Jan Gotfryd Hall (?), active 1678–1700. Silver, partly gilt, repoussé, chiseled. Height 61.5 cm., width 77.5 cm., weight 2500 grams. Inv. no. 500WIL.

In the center is represented the triumphal entry of King Jan III Sobieski (1642–1696) and Queen Marie Casimire in a baroque, four-horse chariot, led by grooms in Polish costumes, after his victory over the Turks and the liberation of Vienna in 1683. Behind the chariot appears a crowd of Turkish prisoners.

The National Museum of Warsaw, Wilanow Section

60 Jan III Sobieski with his Family

By an unidentified painter of the court circle, turn of the 17th and 18th centuries. Oil on canvas, 73.5 × 108.5 cm. Inscribed on the reverse: *Familie de Jean Sobieski Roi de Pologne.* Inv. no. 1123WIL.

Jan III Sobieski (1624–1696), King of Poland from 1674, defeated the Turks at Chocim in 1673. In 1683 he vanquished the Turkish army besieging Vienna. Against a background of fantastic architecture, the Sobieski family is gathered. On a platform covered with a tapestry carpet with designs of Polish Eagles are Jan III and his Queen Marie Casimire. On his left are his eldest son Jakub and his younger sons Konstanty and Aleksander. On the right foreground is his daughter Teresa Kunegunda. At the Queen's side are Jadwiga Elzbieta Amelia, wife of Jakub, with her infant daughter Maria Leopoldyna.

The National Museum of Warsaw, Wilanow Section

61 Scale Armor

A scaled cuirass with the Ostoja arms. Poland, early 18th century. Steel-scale work on a leather ground, decorations made of copper plates, repoussé and gilded. Used by Polish armored cavalry. This armor once belonged to the Uniechowski family of the Ostoja coat of arms. Height 186 cm. Inv. no. 3939.

The State Art Collection of Wawel Castle, Cracow

JEAN-BAPTISTE OUDRY

Oudry (1686–1755) was a French painter and graphic artist, pupil of Jacques Oudry and Nicolas de Largillière, and member of the Fine Arts Academy from 1719. He painted portraits, still-lifes, hunting trophies, and designed tapestry cartoons. He also directed a manufactory in Beauvais, and was inspector-general of the Royal Manufactory of the Gobelins.

62 Portrait of King Stanislas Leszczynski

Oil on canvas, 104.5 × 87 cm. Signed: *Oudry 1730.* Inv. no. 131472.

The portrait presents Stanislas Leszczynski in a pilgrim's costume of St. James of Compostella, most probably in allusion to his tragic fate. Stanislas Leszczynski was King of Poland from 1704 to 1711, then was forced to leave the throne and his country. His daughter, Maria Leszczynska, became wife of Louis XV in 1725. After the death of Augustus II, Stanislas was again elected king. After a three-year fight for his throne, on the strength of a peace treaty concluded in 1736, he received the life estate of Lorraine and the Principality of Baru, and gave up his rights to the Polish throne. During his reign, Lorraine flourished through a period of unusual development. The King made his residence in Luneville, where his court ranked among the most progressive in Europe at that time. Leszczynski, a highly educated personality, became a patron and maecenas of art. In Nancy, he established an Academy that bore his name. He published numerous works, collected and published in Nancy in 1763, under the title *Oeuvres du Philosophe Bienfaisant. (illustrated)*

The National Museum of Warsaw

63 Sword of Stanislas Augustus Poniatowski

Warsaw, 1764. Blue-hardened steel, colored gold, silver, sapphire, red and white enamel, wood, velvet. Length 91.3 cm., width 15.5 cm., weight 1120 grams. Inv. no. SZM. 6753MN. *(illustrated)*

A two-edged blade, flat, blue-hardened, trimmed with gold on both sides. On one side are the Polish Eagle, alternating with the Lithuanian "Pogon" and with the king's family crest, the "Ciolek," and an inscription *"stanislaus augustus rex dedit anno 1764."* On the reverse are the same inscription and the monogram "SAR" (Stanislas Augustus Rex) under a crown. On the obverse of the guard are medallions with enamel images of the Immaculate Conception and St. Stanislas; on the reverse, an enamel ground bears gold monograms of the king, under a crown. Under the cross, a shield and cartouche bear the Polish emblem and king's arms in enamel. The sheath is covered with crimson velvet, with gold trimming. The sword was specially made for the coronation of the king in 1764, and was included among the insignia of the Order of the White Eagle and the Order of Saint Stanislas. It was used during the investment ceremonies.

The National Museum of Warsaw

64 Chain of the Order of the White Eagle

Warsaw, 1764. Gold, detailed fragments cast, sapphire, and white enamel. Length 93 cm., width 2.8 cm., weight 292 grams. Inv. no. SZM. G751MN. *(illustrated)*

The chain has 24 parts, among them 12 eagles with sceptres and royal insignia separated by 12 ovals encircled by rays. Six of them represent the Immaculate Conception, the other six carry the inscription *"Marya"* on an enamel ground. The Order of the White Eagle, the highest Polish decoration, was established on November 1, 1705, by King Augustus II, the Strong. The supreme authority of the order was always the king himself. This chain was made specially for the coronation in 1764. The slogan of the order was that of the king's *"pro fide lege et grege."* The device of the cavaliers was *"pro fide et rege."* The cavaliers, instead of the chain, wore the decoration on a blue moire ribbon over their arms and a star in the form of a cross on their chests.

The National Museum of Warsaw

65–76 *BERNARDO BELLOTTO*

Bernardo Bellotto, called Canaletto (1720–1780), was a painter of Italian origin, pupil and nephew of the famous Canaletto of Venice. From 1747 he was active at the courts of Augustus III in Dresden, of Maria Theresa in Vienna, and the Bavarian Elector in Munich. From 1767 until his death, he was court painter of Stanislas Augustus in Warsaw. He introduced in Poland the art of veduta *and genre painting. It was on the king's order that he painted a cycle of 26 views of Warsaw and its surroundings to decorate the walls of the Royal Palace. His views are precious sources for the study of the plans, architecture, history, and customs of Warsaw, and they provided excellent documents for the reconstruction of monuments ruined during the last war. Canaletto also painted historical scenes in Poland.*

65 *General View of Warsaw from Praga*

Oil on canvas, 172.5 × 261 cm. On the easel is the following inscription: *Prospectus Varsaviae incipiendo de Villa nova usque ad Palatinum Comitis Sa/ piehea cum inclusa parte Pragea trans/ flumen depictus per B. B. de Canaletto/ A° 1770.* Inv. no. 128663.

The picture shows a panorama of Warsaw seen from the right bank of the Vistula on the northeast side. In the foreground is the painter himself, painting this very same view. He is in conversation with Stanislas Augustus Poniatowski. Behind them stand Bellotto's son Lorentzo and his son-in-law, the royal geographer Hermann Karol de Parthess. On the right, in the back, appear a coach and a royal cortège. On the left bank of the Vistula are the suburbs of Praga with the baroque Bernardine Church of Saint Andrew (17th century, demolished in the 20th). Beyond the river, on which many boats may be seen, a vast panorama of the left bank of the city. In the center, a rococo façade (1742) of the Royal Palace with a baroque tower dominating it (1622). To the right are the buildings of the Old and New City with the Gothic Collegiate Church of St. John, later transformed into a Cathedral, an early baroque Jesuit church, the baroque church of the Paulists, that of the Dominicans, and the Church of the Holy Sacrament, as well as the Gothic Church of the Virgin Mary, the baroque church of the Franciscans, and the rococo palace of Sapieha at Zakroczymska Street. Toward the left, starting from the Palace, are the Gothic Bernardine Church of St. Anne, the baroque Church of the Carmelites, and that of the Sisters of the Visitation. Behind, the towers and roof of the Holy Cross Church can be seen. At the left, again, appears the complex of buildings of the Knight's School in the former royal palace, known as the Kazimierzowski Palace, early baroque, rebuilt later, and today the headquarters of the University of Warsaw. Farther behind, appears the Ujazdowski Palace in an early baroque setting, and the meadows stretching as far as the Wilanow.

The National Museum of Warsaw

66 *Krakowskie Przedmiescie Street from the Cracow Gate*

Oil on canvas, 112 × 170 cm., 1767–1768. On the right, bottom, an inscription describing the view and the buildings depicted, with the signature B. B. de Canaletto. Inv. no. 128659. *(illustrated)*

The view was taken from the vicinity of the Royal Palace. On the left, the column of King Sigismund III, erected in 1644 by King Wladislaus IV to commemorate his father. (The work of architect C. Tencalla, the figure of the king was done by C. Molli). In the left corner are the monastery and church of the Bernardines, early baroque, of the beginning of the 17th century, and demolished in the second quarter of the

19th. Farther behind are the first yards of the Krakowski Przedmiescie, the principal street of Warsaw at that time. In the left row of houses is the baroque façade of the Bernardine Church of St. Anne (mid-18th century), farther, the baroque chapel of the Discalced Carmelites, with the Carmelite church in the back, and on the right the towers of the Holy Cross Church. On the corner of the right row is the showy rococo house of the merchant John, reaching as far as the Senatorska Street, rebuilt in the 19th century, ruined during the last war, and reconstructed according to this very picture. The right corner of the picture shows a view to the Palace of the Bishops of Cracow at Miodowa Street, seen through Senatorska Street.

The National Museum of Warsaw

67 View of Krakowskie Przedmiescie from Nowy Swiat Street

Oil on canvas, 84 × 107 cm., 1778. Inv. no. 128665. *(illustrated)*

On the left is the baroque Church of the Holy Cross, the construction of which was started in 1682 by the architect J. Bellotti and finished by Joseph and Jakub Fontana in the mid-18th century. On the right, among burghers' houses, a gate leads to the courtyard of the Knight's School, today housing the University of Warsaw. In the back, the façade of the Carmelite church, then under construction, is seen with its scaffolding.

The National Museum of Warsaw

68 The Carmelite Church

Oil on canvas, 113 × 170 cm., 1780. Inv. no. 128650. *(illustrated)*

A scene on Krakowskie Przedmiescie Street, with a baroque church built in 1643–1701, a late-baroque façade with neo-classical elements of 1761–62, according to the design of the architect E. Szerger. The palace seen on the right was built in 1643–45 for Hetman Stanislas Koniecpolski, probably after C. Tencella's design, and expanded in the mid-18th century, in a late-baroque style, for the Radziwill family. In 1818–19 it was again transformed in a neo-classical style after a design

by P. Aigner, and reconstructed after the last war to serve as the headquarters of the Praesidium of the Council of Ministers.

The National Museum of Warsaw

69 Church of the Sisters of the Visitation

Oil on canvas, 113 × 170 cm., 1780. Inv. no. 128657. *(illustrated)*

A late-baroque church on Krakowskie Przedmiescie Street, built in 1727–34 and 1754–62, following a design of K. Bay's. The façade seen on this canvas was built in the second stage, most probably with the assistance of architect E. Szerger. Close by is a monastery; in the foreground, a market place.

The National Museum of Warsaw

70 Miodowa Street

Oil on canvas, 84 × 107 cm., 1778. Inv. no. 128653. *(illustrated)*

On the left side of the street is the baroque palace of the Bishops of Cracow, from the first half of the 18th century, rebuilt in 1762, and completely reconstructed after the devastation of the last war. Farther back is the neo-classic palace of the banker Tepper, 1774–75, the work of E. Szerger, and next to it the baroque façade of the Church of the Capuchines, built in 1683–92 with funds given by Jan III Sobieski, after a design by A. Locci. On the right side, the baroque palace (mid-18th century) of Jan Klemens Branicki, the Great Hetman of the Crown, Commander-in-Chief of the Polish Army. The palace was most probably the work of Jakub Fontana. It was reconstructed from ruins after the last war, and this very picture served as model. At the end of the street is the Krasinski Palace.

The National Museum of Warsaw

71 Krasinskis Square

Oil on canvas, 116 × 164 cm., 1778. Inv. no. 128656. *(illustrated)*

On the right is the Krasinskis Palace, known as the palace of Rzeczpospolita (Res Publica), built about 1680–99 in classicizing late-baroque form, as designed by the architect Tylman of Gameren, working during the last stage of its construction. Sculptural decorations were for the most part created by A. Schulter. In 1764, the Palace was purchased to serve as the seat of the Government. "Polska" was Poland's formal name then, hence the use of the name "Rzeczypospolita" Palace. Today the Palace serves as headquarters of the National Library. At the back of the square, through which a procession is passing, appears the late-baroque Piarist Church at Dluga Street, and on the corner of Miodowa Street, a rococo building, the Collegium Nobilium, 1743, designed by the architect Jakub Fontana.

The National Museum of Warsaw

72 The Blue Palace

Oil on canvas, 85 × 108 cm., 1779. Inv. no. 128655. *(illustrated)*

In its rococo form, as represented on this canvas, the palace was built in 1726 by the architects D. J. Jauch, J. Z. Deybl, and K. F. Poppelmann for the daughter of King Augustus II, countess Anna Orzelska. The palace was rebuilt in 1812–15 in a neo-classical style, and reconstructed after the destruction of the last war. On the left side is the garden of Mniszech Palace and, farther back, the Church of the Reformed Friars on Senatorska Street.

The National Museum of Warsaw

73 The New City Market Square with the Church of the Holy Sacrament

Oil on canvas, 84 × 106 cm., 1778. Inv. no. 128653. *(illustrated)*

The Church of the Holy Sacrament and the neighboring monastery were built by Tylman of Gameren in 1688–80, in a classicizing baroque style. On the right are the early baroque towers of Saint Benon Church; on the left the Gothic Church of the Virgin Mary (15th century). In the foreground is the market, which was at that time the center of a district of Warsaw called the New City, a district that was already growing up alongside the Old City by the 15th century.

The National Museum of Warsaw

74 The Wilanow Meadows

Oil on canvas, 173 × 246 cm., 1775. Inv. no. 128682. *(illustrated)*

The picture was painted in the vicinity of the Belweder Palace from a buttress over the Vistula. Behind, among the trees, is the villa of Princess Izabella Lubomirska in the Mokotow, 1772, by the architect E. Szerger. On the left is the river; on the right, in the suburbs of Czerniakow, the baroque church built by Tylman of Gameren, late in the 17th century; on the horizon appear the palace and church in Wilanow.

The National Museum of Warsaw

75 The Palace of Wilanow

Oil on canvas, 117 × 164 cm., 1777. Inv. no. 210579. *(illustrated)*

Wilanow is situated several miles to the south of Warsaw, and is today within the city boundaries. In 1677, Jan III Sobieski bought it, together with the neighboring villages. From the Sobieski family the palace passed in 1720 to the Sieniawskis family, then to Czartoryski, Lubomirski, Potocki, and Branicki, successively. Since 1945 it has formed a section of the National Museum of Warsaw. The palace was rebuilt several times. The baroque form, as represented on the canvas, was added and took form during the reign of Jan III Sobieski, under the supervision of the architect A. Locci. Its reconstruction took place from about 1720 until the early 'thirties of the 18th century, directed by G. Spazio and, from 1726, by J. Deybel in co-operation with Jozef Fontana. The view presented here is of the upper and lower parts of a baroque park created during the reign of Jan III Sobieski under the direction of A. Boy. The lower wall of the terrace was not yet finished when the painting was being done, and it is therefore a creation of Bellotto's phantasy.

The National Museum of Warsaw

76 The Election of Stanislas Augustus

Oil on canvas, 175 × 250 cm. On the right side, an inscription explains the landscape in the picture and the names and functions of the persons represented, as well as the signature of the painter: *PEint par Bernardo Bellotto de Canaletto l' an 1778.* Inv. no. 128666. *(illustrated)*

From the late 16th century, Polish kings were elected by the entire nobility. The election was held in the fields between Wola (today a part of Warsaw) village and Warsaw. This is why the painter has presented a vast plain near Wola, and placed his action there. In the center of the picture is a temporary wooden barn for the senators. Close by are the tents of foreign representatives; nobility from various districts of Poland with their flags are gathered around the so-called "knights' circle." In the foreground are, from left to right: royal courtiers shaking hands; a man in a four-cornered hat, who may be Colonel Arnold Anastazy Byszewski; the Voivode of the Plock district, Jozef Podoski, on horseback, handing over the ballots of his district to the marshal of the election Seym [Diet], Jozef Sosnowski; and the Primate Wladyslaw Lubienski is seen in his coach. The horse in a magnificent harness is probably destined for the elected. Close by, a courtier mounts his horse for departure. Behind, in a coach, is Princess Eleanora Czartoryska, wife of Fryderyk Michal, Great Chancellor of Lithuania. At the bottom right corner, under a tent, appear Bellotto and his three daughters. With them are the court architect Dominik Merlini and, in front of the tent, Antoni Crutta, translator of the Chancellory of the Crown.

The National Museum of Warsaw

POMPEO GIROLAMO BATONI

Pompeo Batoni (1708–1787) was an Italian painter of the late baroque and early neo-classical period. He chose Raphael as his model, returning at the same time to the antique. He painted mythological, religious, and allegorical subjects. Batoni was especially the painter of European royalty and aristocracy.

77 Portrait of the Princess Lubomirska

Oil on canvas, 65 × 53.5 cm. *Signed: Pompeo Batoni pin. Rom. 1780.* Inv. no. Wil. 1695. *(illustrated)*

Aleksandra, Princess Lubomirska (1702–1787), was the wife of the count Stanislaw Kostka-Potocki, whose portrait by David is also included in this exhibition (no. 79). Aleksandra Potocka is represented here as the muse Melpomene, and wears the attribute of a tragic mask on a golden chain. The picture was painted during the Potockis' visit to Rome in 1780.

The National Museum of Warsaw, Wilanow Section

78 Portrait of Izabella Lubomirska

Oil on canvas, 65 × 53.5 cm. *Signed: Pompeo Batoni pinse Rome 1780.* Inv. no. Wil. 1694. *(illustrated)*

Izabella Lubomirska, Countess Potocka (d.1783), was the sister of Aleksandra Potocka (see no. 77), and the wife of Ignacy Potocki (1750–1809), writer and political leader of the reform group during the reign of Stanislas Augustus. He was co-author of the Constitution of the 3rd of May, and the author of many works, among them *The Institution and Decay of the 3rd May Constitution.* Izabella, depicted as the muse Polihymnia, holds a roll of music.

The National Museum of Warsaw, Wilanow Section

JACQUES-LOUIS DAVID

David (1748–1825) was the most outstanding painter of French neo-classicism. During the Revolution he was a member of the Convention and a friend of Marat. During the Empire he became court painter to Napoleon. He gained his fame with antique subjects. His portraits, remarkable for their realism and lively setting, form a most valuable part of his work.

79 Portrait of Stanislaw Kostka Potocki

Oil on canvas, 304 × 218 cm. Signed: *David 1781.* Inv. no. Wil. 596.

Count Stanislaw Kostka Potocki (1752–1821) was an outstanding statesman, writer, political leader, minister of Religious Beliefs and Public Education (1815–18), architect, historian, and theoretician of art—in short, one of the most enlightened and progressive figures in all Polish history. David probably began this portrait in Rome, in 1780, and finished it in 1781 in Paris. The picture was exhibited at the Salon of 1781 and received most favorable critical opinions. Diderot referred to it: *"Superbe tableau d'une couleur moins sombre que les autres"* (D.Diderot, *Oeuvres completes*, vol. XII, Paris 1876, p. 64). *(illus.)*

The National Museum of Warsaw

ANGELICA KAUFFMANN

Angelica Kauffmann (1741–1807) was born in Switzerland, and worked mainly in Italy and in England. She lived in Rome from 1782, and played an important part in the city's artistic life. She painted mythological, religious, and allegorical subjects, but her fame rests principally on her many portraits.

80 Portrait of Helena Mecinska

Helena Mecinska, née Stadnicka, is portrayed in a sentimental, neo-classical manner, very characteristic of the artist. The pendant of this portrait was the portrait of the General-Castellan Wojciech Mecinski, husband of Helena, painted by the same artist, and which is now lost. *(illustrated)*

The National Museum of Warsaw

ANDRZEJ LE BRUN

Andrzej Le Brun (1737–1811) was a pupil of J.-B. Pigalle, and also studied at the French Academy in Rome. He was invited by Stanislas Augustus Poniatowski to Warsaw in 1767, and remained in Poland for the rest of his life. Le Brun was the first court sculptor and directed all sculpture works at the Royal Palace in Warsaw. He created many sculptures for the decoration of the Royal Palace, the Lazienki Palace, and other royal buildings, as well as statues and reliefs of antique and historical themes.

81 Bust of Andrzej Lipski

Andrzej Lipski (1572–1631) was Bishop of Cracow and the first Great Chancellor of the Crown. Bronze, marble stand, height 62 cm. Incised on the back: *Iohann Ehrenfrid Dietrich/Goss Mich in Warschau den.29 Januar.1782;* on the front: *Lipski;* on the stand: *Andreas Lipski/ +MDCXXXI.* 1781–1782. Inv. no. 131699. *(illustrated)*

The National Museum of Warsaw

82 Bust of Stanislaw Malachowski

Malachowski (d.1699) was Voivode of Kalisz and the Poznan regions. Bronze, marble stand, height 62 cm. Inscribed on front: *Malachowski;* on the stand: *Sta:Malachowski/ +MDCXCIX.* 1781–1786. Inv. no. 131696.

The National Museum of Warsaw

83 Bust of Prince Jeremi Wisniowiecki

Prince Wisniowiecki (1612–1651) was Voivode of Ruthenia, and father of King Michal Korybut. Bronze, marble stand, height 62 cm. Inscribed on the bust: *Koribut Wisniowiecki;* on the stand: *Hie:Wisniowiecki/ +MDCLI.* 1770–1786. Inv. no. 131691. *(illustrated)*

The National Museum of Warsaw

GIACOPO MONALDI

Monaldi (1730–1798), a sculptor of Italian origin, was invited to Warsaw in 1768 by Stanislas Augustus. He was court sculptor and also worked for personalities associated with the court. Monaldi created many sculptures for the Royal Palace, the Lazienki Palace, and other royal buildings in Warsaw. He made the statues of the saints decorating the façade of St. Anne's Church in Warsaw, as well as allegorical statues of antique and religious subjects, statues of historical heroes, medallions of famous people, and tomb monuments.

84 Bust of Stefan Czarniecki

Stefan Czarniecki (1599–1665), Voivode of the Kiev region, was Field Hetman of the Crown, and a most brilliant commander. Bronze, marble stand, height 61 cm. Inscribed on the stand: *Stefan Czarniecki/ MDCXV.* 1781–1786. Inv. no. 212760.

The National Museum of Warsaw

JEAN-PIERRE NORBLIN DE LA GOURDAINE

Norblin (1745–1830) was educated in Paris and brought to Poland by Prince Adam Czartoryski. He worked from 1774 to 1804 as the Prince's court painter in his residence at Powazki, near Warsaw, and, about 1790, settled in Warsaw. He began in Poland with decorative park scenes in the style of Watteau; later, as a graphic artist, he derived his subjects from Poland's political, social, and traditional life, taking a vivid interest in all historical developments. It was in this field that he educated many of his pupils.

85 A Party on the Lake

Oil on canvas, 140.5 × 206.5 cm., about 1785. Inv. no. 212668.

This is one of the series of five paintings created by Norblin as decorations for the palace of Princess Izabela Czartoryska at Powazki, near Warsaw. All five paintings have been preserved. The atmosphere of the painting, and its technique and coloring, link it with French rococo painting, particularly that of Watteau. *(illustrated)*

The National Museum of Warsaw

K. ALEKSANDROWICZ

Having finished his studies in Warsaw, the artist worked between 1777–1794 at princely courts, making portraits of his contemporaries and copies of old paintings. Konstanty Aleksandrowicz' painting shows the influence of Bacciarelli, with a marked return to the traditions of Sarmatian portraiture.

86 Portrait of Karol Radziwill

Oil on canvas, 81.5 × 64.5 cm., about 1785. Inv. no. 101619. *(illus.)*

The portrait shows an accurate and firm characterization of the model, a flat and linear painting technique, and little differentiation of coloring, making it a good example of Polish "Sarmatian" portrait (see nos. 55, 57, 58, 87, 93–108). Karol Radziwill, known as "Panie Kochanku" [Dear Sir], from his habit of repeating the salutation constantly, was a typical representative of the Polish Sarmatian trend. He is posed here in a sapphire kontusz-uniform of a general, with silver embroideries and epaulets, in a prince's coat of red and ermine, with a great ribbon and star of the Polish Order of the White Eagle, the Polish Order of Saint Stanislas, and the Russian Order of Saint Andrew.

The National Museum of Cracow

FRANCISZEK SMUGLEWICZ

Smuglewicz (1745–1807) studied in Warsaw and in Rome, where he gained an excellent position in art circles. He returned to Poland in 1784, and lived at first in Warsaw. In 1797 he moved to Vilno, where he held the chair of design and painting at the University, and became in fact the creator of the "Vilno School." The artist painted compositions from the antique and the Bible, historical scenes, genre subjects, religious themes, and a few portraits. He exerted a considerable influence on Polish painters of the turn of the 18th and 19th centuries.

87 The Prozor Family

Oil on canvas, 182 × 144 cm., 1789. Inv. no. 130885.

The picture is a posthumous apotheosis of Jozef Prozor, Voivode of Witebsk. In the center, under a cypress tree, on a stone block, is a medallion with the portrait and the inscription "Jozef Prozor Woiewoda Witebski." Ludwika, daughter-in-law of the deceased, places a wreath of everlasting on the picture. Karol, son of Jozef Prozor, points to the inscription incised on the tree trunk, a verse from the poem by Karpinski devoted to the deceased: *"Zyl dla nas wiek swoy caly/ Nieba go nam zabraly/ Lecz zostawil przyklad cnoty/ Oycze: My tak nie sieroty."* [He devoted to us all his life. Heaven has taken him now. He has left us his virtue as a model. So, we have not been orphaned.] Around the medallion is gathered the Pozor family. From left to right are: Franciczek Bukaty, in a red uniform; Stanislaw Jelski, in a Polish costume; Karol, in a uniform of a general of the Polish army of 1792–94; Ignacy, in a golden dress coat; and Ludwika Prozorowa, née Szujska, wife of Karol. In the foreground are the children of Karol and Ludwika, Jozef and Marianna. The picture links the features of style typical of Sarmatian portraiture with those of official court portraiture.

The National Museum of Warsaw

MARCELLO BACCIARELLI

Bacciarelli (1731–1818) was educated in Rome, became court painter to Augustus III in Dresden, and later to Maria Theresa in Vienna. He was invited to Poland by Stanislas Augustus and settled there in 1766. He was appointed court painter and general director of royal buildings and played an outstanding role as adviser and main executive of the king's artistic policy. He also directed the painting studio at the royal palace, where he educated many Polish painters. He painted many portraits of the king, as well as of his courtiers, and decorated the royal residences with large compositions based on allegorical, mythological, historical, or religious themes.

88 Portrait of Stanislas Augustus Poniatowski

Oil on canvas, 71 × 57 cm., about 1790. Inv. no. 24468. *(illustrated)*
Stanislas Augustus Poniatowski (1732–1798), the last king of Poland,

reigned from 1764 to 1795. He was one of the most enlightened rulers of his time, well-known as a patron of the arts and protector of science.

The National Museum of Warsaw

JOZEF PESZKA

The artist was educated in Cracow, Warsaw, and Vilno. He traveled widely, and worked in Warsaw, Russia, and Eastern Poland. In 1813 he settled in Cracow, where he was first professor and then director of the School of Fine Arts. He painted mainly portraits and group portraits of the aristocracy, nobility, and the bourgeoisie. The most precious among his portraits are those depicting the leaders of the Four Year Seym [Diet], 1788–1792.

89 Portrait of Stanislaw Kubicki

Oil on canvas, 155 × 111 cm., 1790–91. Inv. no. 2689.

Kubicki (d.1809) was captain of the Lithuanian troops, Livonia's deputy to the Four Year Seym, and author of comedies presented on the Warsaw stage. He is painted in the kontusz-uniform of a vice-brigadier of the national cavalry, with the text of a Seym speech in his hand. Kubicki was a member of the reform party, and supported the demands of the townsfolk. The portrait was ordered by the Council of the City of Warsaw on the initiative of its president Dekert, as one of a series of portraits of well-known personalities of the Seym period.

The National Museum of Warsaw

JOZEF GRASSI

Grassi (1758–1838) was educated in Vienna, and came to Warsaw on the invitation of Stanislas Augustus in 1791. He had close contacts with the Polish patriotic party and painted the portraits of aristocratic leaders of the reform party and of several national heroes, like Tadeusz Kosciuszko and Prince Jozef Poniatowski. From 1795 he worked in Vienna and Dresden, where he was appointed a professor at the Acad-

emy of Fine Arts in 1800. His elegant idealized portraits, with their soft modelling, show the influence of English painting.

90 Portrait of Tadeusz Kosciuszko

Oil on canvas, 112 × 90 cm., 1792. Inv. no. 189046. (illustrated)

Hero of Polish national struggles for independence and democracy, general, and head of the Insurrection of 1794, Kosciuszko (1746–1817) was the first to issue orders for improving the lot of the peasants. In 1776–83, he took part in the American War of Independence. As an American general, he created the fortifications at Saratoga and West Point. This is one of several portraits of Kosciuszko created by Grassi, and was copied by many of his contemporaries and later painters. Kosciuszko is represented here as the heroic national leader. The painter, following popular sentiment, has glorified the chief by adding armor, sword, and a helmet with laurel.

The National Museum of Warsaw

91 Sceptre of Stanislas Augustus Poniatowski

Warsaw, 1792. An aquamarine of greenish-blue color with endomorphs, rock crystal, gold setting, and chiseled and engraved casting. Length 58 cm., diameter 3.5 cm., weight 650 grams. Inv. no. SZM. 3283MN.

The sceptre dates to the last years of the king's reign, the times of the Four Year Seym, when important political and social reforms were undertaken, which found their expression in the new, progressive constitution adopted on May 3rd, 1791. (illustrated)

The National Museum of Warsaw

KAZIMIERZ WOJNIAKOWSKI

Wojniakowski (1771–1812) was a pupil of Marcello Bacciarelli. He lived and painted in Warsaw, mainly portraits, but also park scenes, religious subjects, and historical compositions. He was involved in the insurrection of 1794, and made portraits of the leaders of the struggle.

92 Portrait of General Jozef Kossakowski

Oil on canvas, 57 × 48 cm., 1794. Inv. no. II–280. (illustrated)

Jozef Kossakowski (1771–1840), deputy to the Four Year Seym, was one of the leaders of the Kosciuszko Insurrection. This portrait is of a genre connected with the heroic struggles for independence: it shows a realistic approach of the artist to his model, not lacking, however, some accents of romantic treatment.

The National Museum of Cracow

93–108 POLISH COSTUMES

Zupan was a traditional Polish male costume. It was a long robe with narrow sleeves, not split at the back, but pleated from the waist down and fastened at the front with hooks and eyes. Late in the sixteenth century the kontusz was introduced, an outer robe worn over the zupan, with split and tucked-up sleeves showing a colored lining. Zupan and kontusz were of a length reaching to below the knees. As belts, solidly made silk waistbands with silver or gold thread were worn, and were known as Polish waist sashes. The nobility wore their sashes on the kontusz; burghers, who did not wear the kontusz, wore them on their zupans. This Polish costume was an expression of a trend in Polish culture known as the "Sarmatian" trend. (See also nos. 55, 57, 58, 86, 87). This trend was created by a theory, popular since the 16th century, that the Poles originated from the ancient Sarmatians. The "Sarmatian" culture was regarded as separate and independent of Western Europe. This view was strongest during the reign of King Jan III Sobieski, who defeated the Turks at Vienna in 1683. Frequent wars and commerce with the Near East developed an oriental taste in the Sarmatian trend, and influenced Polish costume in that direction. Kontusz and zupan were worn in Poland until the beginning of the nineteenth century. The dress of Western Europe was also worn during this same period. Waist sashes to match the kontusz, richly ornamented and made of colorful silks with silver or gold thread, were at first imported from the East. However, with the growing demand, manufactories were established in Poland in the first half of the eighteenth century. There were nearly thirty of them by the second half of the century. The most famous manufactories in the eighteenth century were those of Stanislawow, Buczacz, Sluck, Grodno, Warsaw, Lipkow, Kobylka, Cracow, and Gdansk. Among the well-known weavers who signed their work one might mention Jan and Leon Mazdzarski working at the Radziwill manufactory in Sluck; Paschalis Jakubowicz, owner of the manufactories in Lipkow and Warsaw; and the Cracow weavers Franciszek Maslowski, Antoni Pucilowski, and Daniel Chmielewski. Polish waist sashes were at first modeled after Eastern patterns and made by Armenian weavers. Toward the middle of the eighteenth century, however, when Polish artisans began production, styles began to yield to clients' tastes, and acquired features of a separate, native art, remarkable for the arrangement of plant motifs and combinations of colors.

93 Kontusz and Zupan

Poland, 18th century. Wool, silk, 119 × 35 cm.; silk 112.5 × 37 cm. Inv. no. 73974.

The National Museum of Warsaw

94 Kontusz and Zupan

Poland, 18th century. Wool, silk, 125 × 32 cm.; silk 125 × 33 cm. Worn with the Order of the White Eagle. Inv. no. 77037. *(illustrated)*

The National Museum of Warsaw

95 Sash

Lipkow, manufactory of Paschalis Jakubowicz, second half of the 18th century. Four-patterned, silk, gold thread, 322 × 34.8 cm., signed *Paschalis.* Inv. no. 156603.

The National Museum of Warsaw

96 Sash

Grodno, manufactory of Antoni Tyzenhauz, second half of the 18th century. Double-pattern, silk, silver thread, 356 × 28.5 cm. Inv. no. 31700. *(illustrated)*

The National Museum of Warsaw

97 Sash

Lipkow, manufactory of Paschalis Jakubowicz, second half of the 18th century. Four-patterned, silk, gold thread, 354 × 37.2 cm., signed *Paschalis.* Inv. no. 156564.

The National Museum of Warsaw

98 Sash

Sluck, Radziwill manufactory, 18th century. Double-pattern, silk, gold thread, 339 × 29 cm., signed *Me fecit Sluciae.* Inv. No. 156576.

The National Museum of Warsaw

99 Sash

Lipkow, manufactory of Paschalis Jakubowicz, second half of the 18th century. Double-pattern, silk, silver thread, 379 × 36 cm., signed *Paschalis.* Inv. no. 156592.

The National Museum of Warsaw

100 Sash

Sluck, Radziwill manufactory, second half of the 18th century. Four-patterned, silk, gold thread, 437 × 36 cm., signed *Sluck.* Inv. no. 156353.

The National Museum of Warsaw

101 Sash

Lipkow, manufactory of Paschalis Jakubowicz, second half of the 18th century. Four-patterned, silk, silver and gold thread, 354 × 37 cm., signed *Paschalis*. Inv. no. 156605.

The National Museum of Warsaw

102 Sash

Cracow, manufactory of Franciszek Maslowski, late 18th century. Four-patterned, silk, gold thread, 476 × 38 cm., signed *Fecit Cracoviae Franciscus Maslowski*. Inv. no. IV.T.2390.

The National Museum of Cracow

103 Sash

Cracow, manufactory of Franciszek Maslowski, late 18th century. Four-patterned, silk, 361 × 29.5 cm., signed *Franciscus Maslowski*. Inv. no. IV.T.2360.

The National Museum of Cracow

104 Sash

Cracow, manufactory of Antoni Pucilowski, late 18th century. Four-patterned, silk, 371 × 35 cm., signed *A. Pucilowski*. Inv. no. IV.T.-2363.

The National Museum of Cracow

105 Sash

Cracow, late 18th century. Double pattern, silk, 382 × 34.5 cm. Inv. no. IV.T.2367.

The National Museum of Cracow

106 Sash

Cracow, manufactory of Daniel Chmielewski, late 18th century. Four-patterned, silk, gold thread, 413 × 38 cm., signed *DC*. Inv. no. IV.T.-2371.

The National Museum of Cracow

107 Sash

Cracow, manufactory of Franciszek Maslowski, late 18th century. Four-patterned, silk, 350 × 29 cm., signed *Franciscus Maslowski*. Inv. no. IV.T.2485.

The National Museum of Cracow

108 Polish Waist Sash

Sluck, Radziwill manufactory, 18th century. Four-patterned, silk, gold thread, 340 × 35 cm., signed *Sluck*. Inv. no. 128594.

The National Museum of Warsaw

109 Tapestry Carpet with Oginiec Arms

Poland, the manufactory of Oginskis in Sokolowo, second half of the 18th century. Wool, 354 × 273 cm. Inv. no. 2072.

This carpet with the Oginskis coat of arms is a typical example of Polish tapestry carpets of the 18th century. The tradition dates back to the 15th century; in the 16th century "Mazowieckie" tapestries and "Polonaise" rugs were famous. From the middle of the 17th century, the art of making tapestry carpets developed along Persian and Turkish techniques and models. Soon, however, foreign models were transformed into national ones by local artisans.

The State Art Collection of Wawel Castle, Cracow

JAN ANTONI BLANK

Blank (1785–1884) was born in Olsztyn in the Mazury (Eastern Prussia), and educated in Warsaw and Dresden. He was a highly respected teacher, taught many pupils, and was a leader in the artistic life of Poland. From 1819, he was professor in the Fine Arts department of the University of Warsaw. He represents the neo-classical trend in Polish painting, and in this style produced mythological and religious compositions and portraits, mainly of bourgeois intellectuals.

110 Portrait of the Artist with His Family

Oil on canvas, 206 × 147 cm., 1825. Inv. no. 126360. (illustrated)

At the clavichord is the wife of the artist; on the left are their two daughters. The artist himself leans in through the window.

The National Museum of Warsaw

WALENTY WANKOWICZ

Wankowicz (1799–1842) was educated in Vilno and St. Petersburg, where he was awarded medals for historical painting. He worked in Minsk and Vilno, but in 1841 settled in Paris. He was close to Adam Mickiewicz and painted portraits of many well-known figures, among them the poet Alexander Pushkin.

111 Portrait of Adam Mickiewcz

Oil on canvas, 148 × 125 cm., 1828. Inv. no. 46575. (illustrated)

Adam Mickiewicz (1798–1855) was Poland's greatest poet of the romantic era. This portrait is one of the many the artist devoted to the poet, during the years 1823–1829. Mickiewicz is here presented in a romantic landscape in the mountains of the Crimean coast. The poet rests in a romantic attitude on the Judah rock, where he composed his Crimean sonnets, published in 1826.

The National Museum of Warsaw

ALEKSANDER KOKULAR

Kokular (1793–1846) was educated in Warsaw, Vienna, and Rome. He was professor in the School of Fine Arts in Warsaw, and one of the main exponents of neo-classicism in Polish painting. He was also a collector and one of the first antiquarians in Warsaw. He painted portraits, as well as compositions on antique and religious themes, imbuing them with cool and regular forms.

112 Portrait of the Artist in His Apartment

Oil on canvas, 55 × 72.5 cm., about 1830. Inv. no. 231641. (illustrated)

The National Museum of Warsaw

WINCENTY KASPRZYCKI

Kasprzycki (1802–1849) was educated in Warsaw and Vilno. He was one of those brilliant painters who cultivated the art of landscape and vedute during the first half of the 19th century. He painted a series of views from the Wilanow residence for the count Aleksander Potocki.

113 View of Wilanow Palace

Oil on canvas, 101 × 146 cm., signed Kasprzycki malowal 1833. Inv. no. 181466. (illustrated)

The palace, with a guardhouse on the right, was built for Izabella Lubomirska in 1775–78 (see also no. 75). The baroque entrance gate dates from the time of Sobieski. On the left are two hunters under a tree; in the center is count Aleksander Potocki on horseback with a groom in attendance.

The National Museum of Warsaw

114 View of Morysinek

Oil on canvas, 101 × 145 cm., signed Kasprzycki 1834. Inv. no. 181469. (illustrated)

Morysinek is connected with Wilanow park, on the other side of the Wilanow canal. Morysinek was created by Aleksandra, née Lubomirska, wife of Stanislaw Potocki (see no. 77), early in the 19th century. It was named after her grandson, Maurycy Potocki. The main building, a small palace with a rotunda, was built in 1811 after designs by P. Aigner and St. Kostka Potocki. A neo-Gothic summerhouse stands on the bank of the canal.

The National Museum of Warsaw

JAN NEPOMUCEN GLOWACKI

Glowacki (1802–1846) studied in Cracow, Vienna, Munich, and Rome. He taught design in Cracow, and was a professor of landscape painting in the School of Fine Arts. Although he painted other subjects, as well as portraits, he was most outstanding for his landscape painting, and was the first to paint scenes in the Polish mountains.

115 Morskie Oko in the Tatras

Oil on canvas, 57 × 48 cm., about 1837. Inv. no. II-52. Morskie Oko lake is in the heart of the Tatra mountains. *(illustrated)*

The National Museum of Cracow

PIOTR MICHALOWSKI

Michalowski (1800–1855) was the most outstanding Polish painter during the first half of the nineteenth century, and the chief representative of romanticism in Polish painting. He was an excellent painter of equestrian subjects; in his portraits, he equalled the greatest European masters. He was also a jurist, a naturalist, and a humanist; he filled important state posts with distinction. During his stay in Paris in 1832–33 he studied with N. R. Charlet. At that time he had already become famous and gained appreciation in Paris and London. His painting was influenced by his contemporaries, most brilliantly by the French romantics Géricault and Delacroix. His links with old masters, particu-

larly Velazquez, can also be traced. He painted battle and historical scenes, mostly from the Napoleonic wars, as well as portraits.

116 Man in a Biretta

Oil on canvas. 69.5 × 57 cm. Inv. no. II-148.

Portrait of an unknown man in a red cape and biretta, sometimes called "The Cardinal." The cape covers an underpainting of a girl's head with a shock of black hair.

The National Museum of Cracow

117 Group Portrait

Oil on canvas. 72 cm. × 118 cm. Inv. no. II-180.

The National Museum of Cracow

118 Portrait of Maksymilian Oborski

Oil on canvas, 89 × 62 cm. Inv. no. 308432.

Oborski was a cousin and friend of the artist.

The National Museum of Cracow

119 Charge at Samosierra Gorge

Oil on canvas, 106 × 71 cm. Inv. no. II-151.

Depicting the famous charge of the third squadron of the Polish light cavalry regiment of Napoleon's guard during his Spanish campaign on November 30, 1808.

The National Museum of Cracow

120 Old Man from a Village

Oil on canvas, 60.5 × 46 cm. Inv. no. 180820. *(illustrated)*

One of the artist's most remarkable peasant portraits.

The National Museum of Cracow

121 Krakusi

Oil on canvas, 60 × 90 cm. Signed: *Piotr Michalowski.* Inv. no. 135407.

This painting is one of the most accurate representations of peasant-soldiers in Polish art. The "Krakusi" were peasants of the Cracow district, who took part in the insurrection led by Kosciuszko, the November Insurrection, and other revolutionary movements.

The National Museum of Cracow

BONAWENTURA DABROWSKI

Dabrowski (1807–1862) studied in Warsaw, where he was a participant in the November Insurrection of 1831. He worked in Warsaw, where he painted portraits of many figures from the bourgeois circles.

122 Portrait of Pawel Pelizzaro

Oil on canvas, 96 × 73 cm., 1838. Inv. no. 183750. *(illustrated)*

One of the most typical bourgeois portraits of the Warsaw scene of the second quarter of the 19th century. Pelizzaro owned a picture shop at Krakowski Przedmiescie Street. The portrait won a gold medal at the exhibition of Fine Arts in Warsaw in 1838.

The National Museum of Warsaw

JAN CHRUCKI

Chrucki (1810–1885) finished his studies in St. Petersburg. On his re-turn to Poland in 1845, he lived in Vilno, where he painted still lifes, portraits, interiors, and landscapes.

123 Portrait of Michal Jozef Romer

Oil on canvas, 57.5 × 49.5 cm., signed *Malowal z natury J. Chrucki. Vilno 1847.* Inv. no. 189130. *(illustrated)*

Romer (1778–1853) was President of Vilno in 1812, President of the Education Commission of the University of Vilno in 1819, member of the Patriotic Association, and a political and social leader.

The National Museum of Warsaw

HENRYK RODAKOWSKI

Rodakowski (1823–1894) studied in Vienna and Paris, and was the most outstanding Polish portrait painter of his time. He lived for over twenty years in Paris.

124 Portrait of the Artist's Mother

Oil on canvas, 130 × 95 cm., signed *H. Rodakowski 1853.* Inv. no. 160. *(illustrated)*

This portrait is a masterpiece of Polish painting. When it was exhibited at the Paris Salon of 1853, it won great appreciation. Delacroix, having seen the picture, entered a note in his diary *"j'ai vu un véritable chef-d'oeuvre"* (*Journal de Eugène Delacroix,* vol. II, 1850–1854, Paris, 1893, p. 156).

The Museum of Art of Lodz

LEON KAPLINSKI

Kaplinski (1826–1873) was a painter, graphic artist, poet, and political leader. A member of the Democratic Association, he took part in the patriotic movements of 1846. During 1848–1870, he was an émigré, in Paris. He was a friend of the leader of the Polish émigrés, Prince Adam Czartoryski, and of Zygmunt Krasinski, one of the most outstanding poets of the romantic era. Kaplinski painted historical pictures, allegories, landscapes, and portraits, being greatly influenced by Rodakowski in this field.

125 Portrait of Seweryn Markiewicz

Oil on canvas, 53 × 42 cm., signed *L.K.1860*. Inv. no. 183759. *(illus.)*

Markiewicz (1830–1870), a jurist, took part in the 1863 Insurrection.

The National Museum of Warsaw

JAN MATEJKO

Poland's greatest historical painter, Matejko (1838–1893), was educated in Cracow, Munich, and Vienna. He refused the post of director of the School of Fine Arts in Prague, and in 1873 was appointed director of the Cracow School of Fine Arts. An ardent patriot, he treated art as a social mission, and in this spirit he created large compositions, in which with a highly suggestive energy he depicted the most important events in Polish history. Matejko also painted portraits, and in 1889–91 worked on the decorations of the Church of the Virgin Mary in Cracow.

126 The Battle at Grunwald

Oil sketch on canvas, 73.5 × 138.3 cm., 1872. Inv. no. 127926.

The battle took place in 1410 on the Grunwald plains. Polish, Lithuanian, and Russian troops fought the Knights of the Cross, supported by German knights. The central figure of the composition is Witold, Great Prince of Lithuania, cousin of the Polish King Wladyslaw Jagiello. On the left is the Grand Master of the Knights of the Cross, Ulrich von Jungingen, a few seconds before his death. On the right, on a hill, King Wladyslaw Jagiello appears with his guards. High above, over the bat-

tle, a banner with the Polish Eagle dominates the fallen banner of the Knights of the Cross.

The National Museum of Warsaw

127 The Sigismund Bell

Oil on wood, 94 × 189 cm., signed *1874 Jan Matejko*. Inv. no. 184735.

The scene is placed in Renaissance Cracow of 1520. In the background is the Royal Castle at Wawel. In the foreground are King Sigismund the Old and his Queen, Bona, surrounded by their court. The successor to the throne, Sigismund Augustus, is presented as a child with his sister Izabela. On the steps of the platform is Stanczyk, the royal jester. The artist has given his own features to the royal clown. On the right, the bell-founder Master Beham directs the operation. Against the scaffolding are the royal lutanist Bekwark and the architect Bartolomeo Berecci, who created the Renaissance decoration of Wawel. The Sigismund Bell still hangs in the tower of Wawel Cathedral, and still sounds on momentous occasions, as during Matejko's funeral, when the great bell tolled the national mourning. *(illustrated)*

The National Museum of Warsaw

ILLUSTRATIONS

1   Chalice and Paten, 11th century

Chalice and Paten, 1238

15   *Crucifix*

6   *Virgin and Child from Kruzlowa*

33   *Horn of Wieliczka Salt Miners*

23   *Tile with King Jan Olbracht*

34   *Sword of Sigismund the Old and Sigismund Augustus*

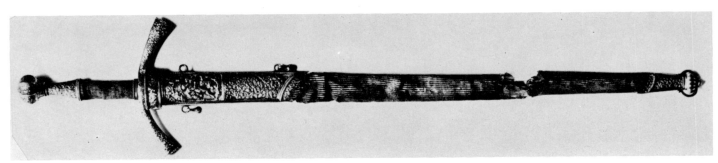

13   *Cross of Princely Crowns*

Opposite:
19   *Chasuble with the Life of St. Stanislas*
12   *Wing from Mikuszowice Altar*

17   *Descent from the Cross*

9

12

35   *Silver Bird*

39   *Wawel Head of a Man*   41   *Wawel Head of a Girl*

36   Nicolaus Copernicus

53

58

54

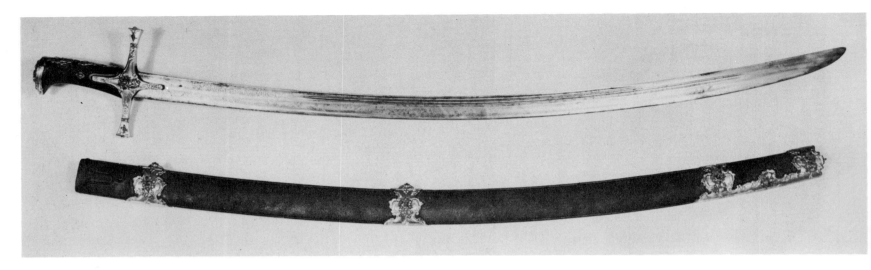

56   *Costume Sabre*

Left: 64   Chain of the Order of the White Eagle

Right: 91   Sceptre of Stanislas Augustus Poniatowski

62   Oudry: King Stanislas Leszczynski

48 *Jagellonian Tapestry*

46 *Jagellonian Verdure Tapestry*

66   *Bellotto: Krakowskie Przedmiescie Street*

69   Bellotto: *Church of the Sisters of the Visitation*

67   *Bellotto: Krakowskie Przedmiescie from Nowy Swiat Street*

72   *Bellotto: The Blue Palace*

70   *Bellotto: Miodowa Street*

71   Bellotto: *Krasinskis Square*

68   *Bellotto: The Carmelite Church*

73   *Bellotto: The New City Market Square*

74   *Bellotto: The Wilanow Meadows*

75   *Bellotto: Palace of Wilanow*

Second Tableau du Champ d'Elsen de Sa Majesté Stanislas Auguste qui fut élu
Roi de Pologne et Grand Duc de Lithuanie par la dieppt... ... peint par Bernardo Belotto
dit Canaletto l'an ... le monde ... ... les derniers relatives et documents avec ... ... des personnes
Le ... ... par ... ... à Sa Excellence Royale le Comte ... ...

79   David: Stanislaw Kostka Potocki

Opposite:
76   Bellotto: Election of Stanislas Augustus

Opposite:

80   A. Kauffmann: Helena Mecinska

90   Grassi: Tadeusz Kosciuszko

78   Batoni: Izabella Lubomirska, Countess Potocka

77   Batoni: Aleksandra, Princess Lubomirska

81   A. LeBrun: Bust of Andrzej Lipski   83   A. LeBrun: Bust of Prince Wisniowiecki

85 *Norblin: Party on the Lake*

Within the image:
ROMER Michał.
Ur: r. 1778. ⅞ Września.
† r. 1853. Stycznia 14.

123   *J. Chrucki: Michal Jozef Romer*

Opposite:
112   *A. Kokular: Portrait of the Artist*

94 *Kontusz and Zupan*

96 *Sash*

88   *Bacciarelli: Stanislas Augustus Poniatowski*   86   *K. Aleksandrowicz: Karol Radziwill*

111   *W. Wankowicz: Adam Mickiewicz*

92   K. Wojniakowski: General Kossakowski

110   J.A. Blank: The Artist with His Family

114   W. Kasprzycki: *View of Morysinek*

113 *W. Kasprzycki: Wilanow Palace*

120 *P. Michalowski: Old Man*

115 *J.N. Glowacki: Morskie Oko in the Tatras*

125 *L. Kaplinski: Seweryn Markiewicz*

122   B. Dabrowski: Pawel Pelizzaro

124   H. Rodakowski: The Artist's Mother

127   J. Matejko: Sigismund Bell

Design: Suzette Morton Zurcher.
Manufactured by The Lakeside Press,
Donnelley Printing Company,
Lancaster, Pennsylvania, a subsidiary
of R. R. Donnelley & Sons Company.